The Singer Songwriter Contemporary Collection

© 2006 by Faber Music Ltd
First published by Faber Music Ltd in 2006
3 Queen Square, London WC1N 3AU

Designed by Lydia Merrills-Ashcroft & Dominic Brookman
Arranged by Chris Hussey & Jack Long
Engraved by Bassline & Camden Music
Compiled by Lucy Holliday
Edited by Lucy Holliday & Olly Weeks

Printed in England by Caligraving Ltd

ISBN 0-571-52540-7

To buy Faber Music publications or to find out about the full range of titles available,
please contact your local music retailer or Faber Music sales enquiries:

Faber Music Ltd, Burnt Mill, Elizabeth Way, Harlow, CM20 2HX England
Tel: +44(0)1279 82 89 82 Fax: +44(0)1279 82 89 83
sales@fabermusic.com fabermusic.com

BAD DAY

Words and Music by Daniel Powter

1. Where is the mo - ment when we need it the most?

You kick up the leaves — and the ma-gic is lost. ___

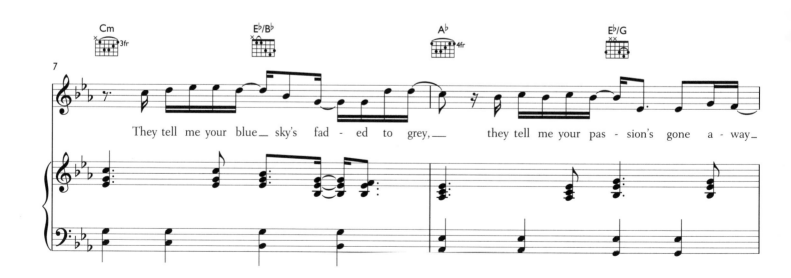

They tell me your blue — sky's fad - ed to grey, ___ they tell me your pas - sion's gone a - way ___

CANNONBALL

Words and Music by Damien Rice

1. There's still a lit-tle bit of your taste in my mouth,

CONCERNING THE UFO SIGHTING NEAR HIGHLAND, ILLINOIS

Words and Music by Sufjan Stevens

DEAR JOHN

Words and Music by Norah Jones and David Ryan Adams

FACTORY

Words and Music by Martha Wainwright

These are not my peo - ple, I should nev - er have come here.

The chick with the dick and the gift for the gab.__ I know a place,__

34

FALLIN'

Words and Music by Alicia Augello-Cook

Freely   N.C.

I keep on fall - in' in _____ *(Vocal ad lib.)* and

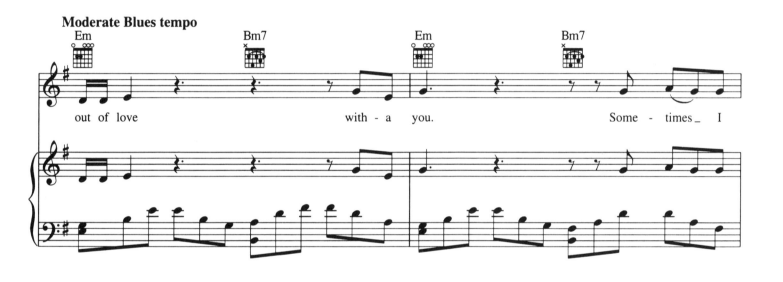

Moderate Blues tempo

Em   Bm7   Em   Bm7

out of love   with - a you.   Some - times_ I

Em   Bm7   Em   Bm7

love you   some - times you make me blue.   Some - times I feel

36

38

GOODBYE MY LOVER

Words and Music by James Blunt and Sacha Skarbek

44

KING OF THE MOUNTAIN

Words and Music by Kate Bush

1. Could you see the aisles of wo - men? Could you see them scream -
2. Could you climb high - er and high - er? Could you climb right ov -

- ing and weep - ing?
- er the top?

HOPE THERE'S SOMEONE

Words and Music by Antony Hegarty

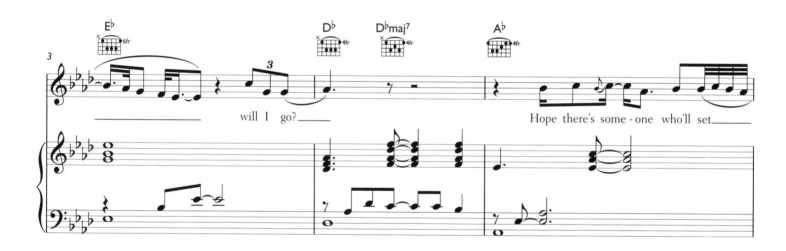

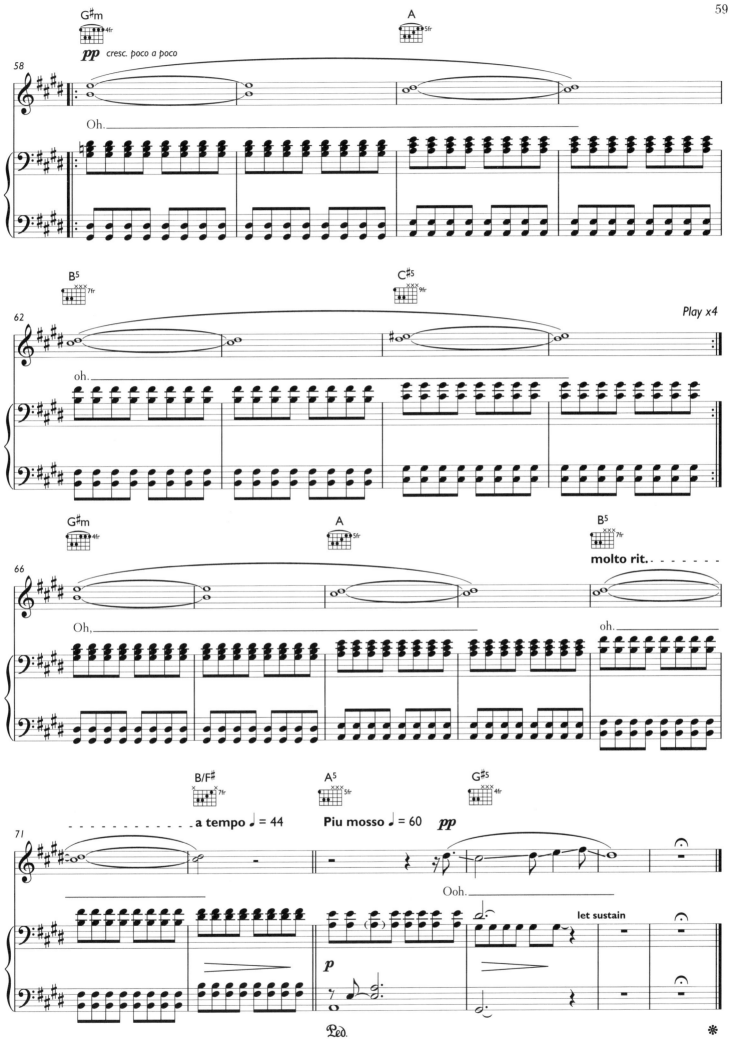

LIKE A STAR

Words and Music by Corinne Bailey Rae

LAST REQUEST

Words and Music by Paolo Nutini, Matt Benbrook and Jim Duguid

70

MY LIFE

Words and Music by Dido Armstrong, Mark Bates and Rollo Armstrong

ORDINARY PEOPLE

Words and Music by John Stephens and Will Adams

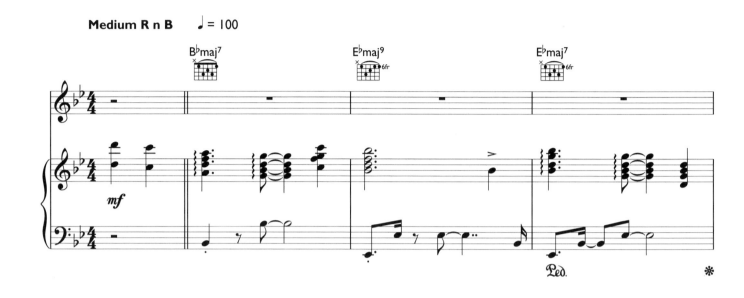

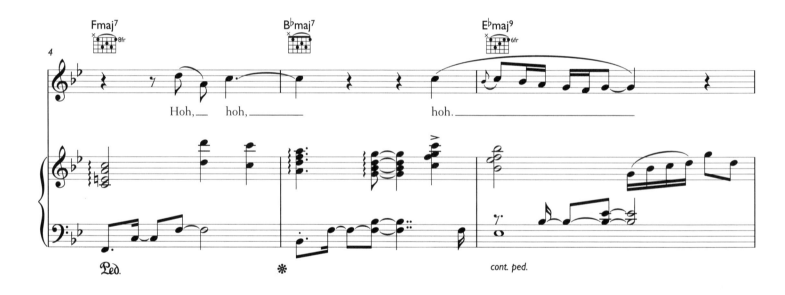

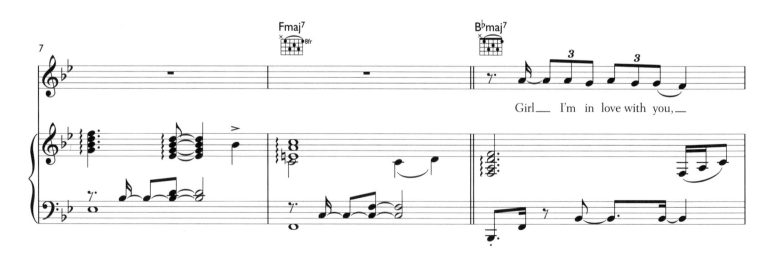

PUT YOUR RECORDS ON

Words and Music by Steven Chrisanthou, John Beck and Corinne Bailey Rae

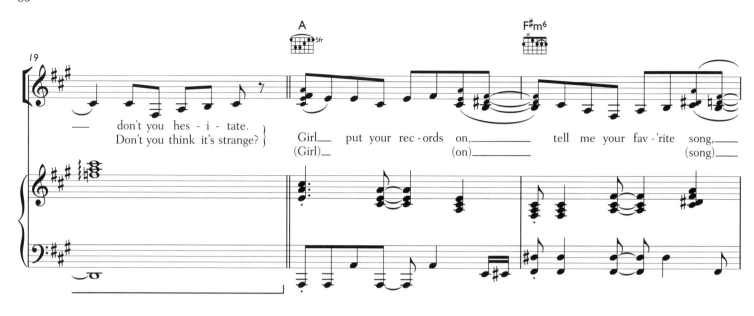

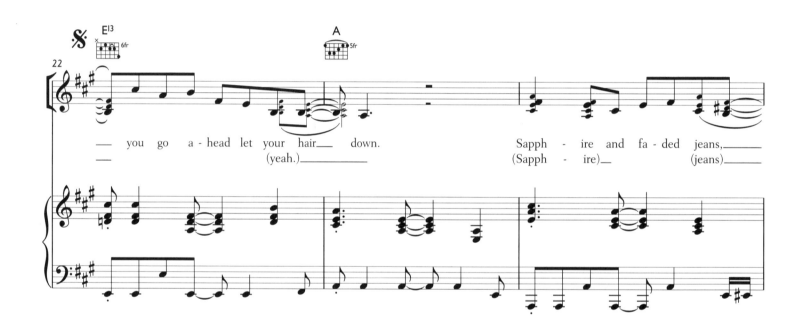

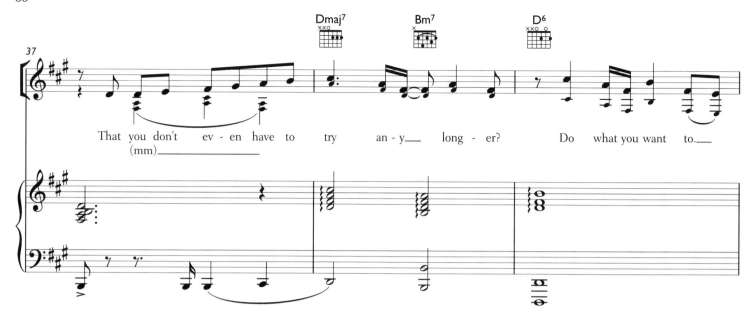

That you don't ev - en have to try an - y___ long - er? Do what you want to.___
(mm)___

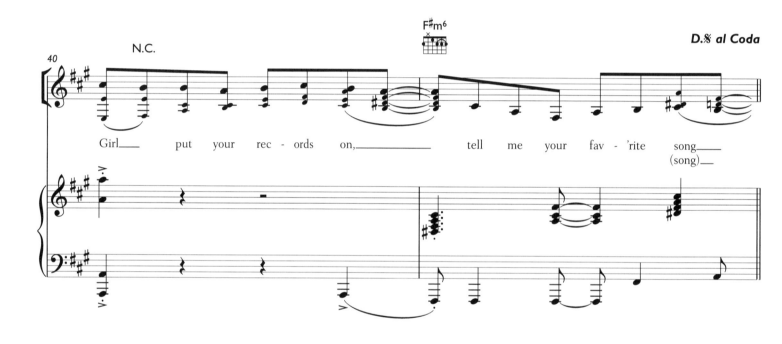

Girl___ put your rec - ords on,___ tell me your fav - 'rite song___
(song)___

hair___ down. Girl___ put your rec-ords on,___ tell me your fav-'rite song,___
(Girl)__ (on)___ (song)___

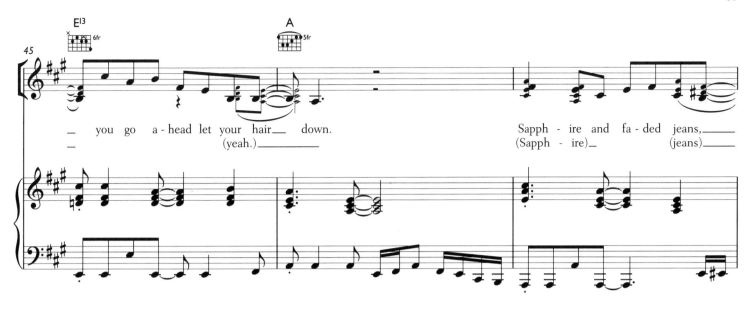

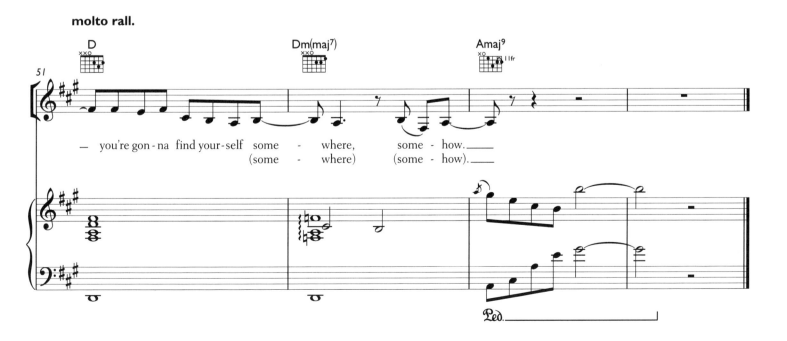

PHOTOGRAPH

Words and Music by Jamie Cullum

SILENT SIGH

Words and Music by Damon Gough

SHE FELL INTO MY ARMS

Words and Music by Ed Harcourt

UNPLAYED PIANO

Words and Music by Damien Rice and Lisa Hannigan

YOU TURN ME AROUND

Words and Music by Matthew Hales

SUNRISE

Words and Music by Norah Jones and Lee Alexander

WAITING FOR A DREAM

Words and Music by Rufus Wainwright

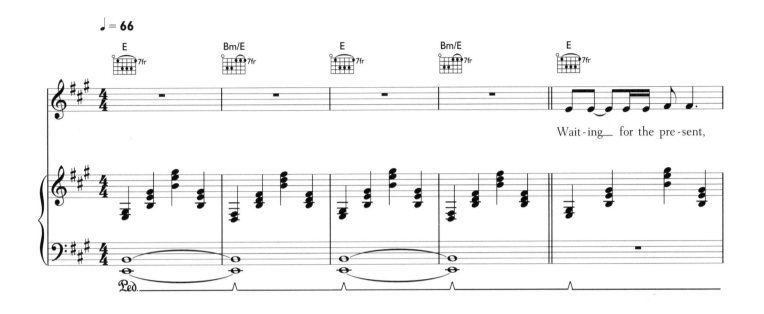

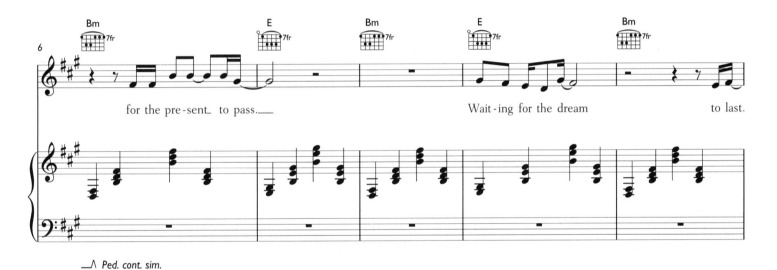

124

wa-ters will not re - flect you.

Af-ter you have turned the co-lour black____ of death or some-thing____ like that.

There's a (1.) fi - re in the pri - o-ry,_____ and it's ru - in-ing this cock-tail par-
(2.) fi - re in the pri - o-ry,_____ and an o - gre in the o - val____

Ped._____ simile

Thirty songs from the most popular contemporary singer songwriters,
arranged for acoustic guitar with full lyrics, strumming patterns and chords.

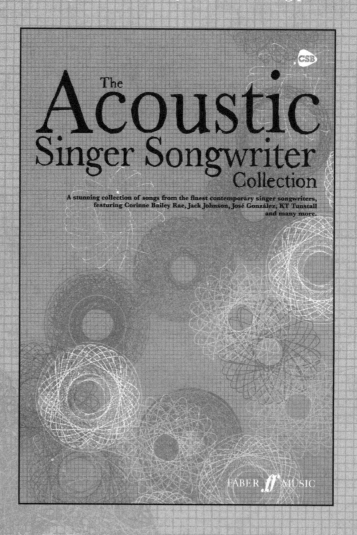

The
Acoustic
Singer Songwriter
Collection

A stunning collection of songs from the finest contemporary singer songwriters,
featuring Corinne Bailey Rae, Jack Johnson, José González, KT Tunstall
and many more.

FABER *ff* MUSIC

Daniel Powter	**Richard Thompson**
Jack Johnson	**Jamie Cullum**
Josh Ritter	**Kathryn Williams**
Sufjan Stevens	**Ryan Adams**
Beth Orton	**Willy Mason**
Damien Rice & Lisa Hannigan	**Corinne Bailey Rae**
Martha Wainwright	**David Ford**
David Gray	**Emiliana Torrini**
Antony & The Johnsons	**K T Tunstall**
José González	**Damien Rice**
James Blunt	**Rufus Wainwright**
Jonathan Rice	**Richard Ashcroft**
Morrissey	**Josh Rouse**
Nizlopi	

FABER *ff* MUSIC